Junior Guest Spot

CHRISTMAS HITS
easy playalong *for* violin

WISE PUBLICATIONS
London/New York/Paris/Sydney/Copenhagen/Madrid/Tokyo

Exclusive Distributors:
Music Sales Limited
8/9 Frith Street,
London W1V 5TZ, England.

Music Sales Pty Limited
120 Rothschild Avenue,
Rosebery, NSW 2018,
Australia.

Order No. AM963149
ISBN 0-7119-8074-8
This book © Copyright 2000 by Wise Publications.

Music compiled and arranged by Paul Honey.
Music processed by Enigma Music Production Services.
Cover photography courtesy George Taylor.

CD produced by Paul Honey.
Instrumental solos by Dermot Crehan.
All guitars by Arthur Dick.
Engineered by Kester Sims.

Your Guarantee of Quality:
As publishers, we strive to produce every book to
the highest commercial standards.
The music has been freshly engraved and the book
has been carefully designed to minimise awkward page
turns and to make playing from it a real pleasure.
Particular care has been given to specifying acid-free,
neutral-sized paper made from pulps which have not
been elemental chlorine bleached.
This pulp is from farmed sustainable forests and
was produced with special regard for the environment.
Throughout, the printing and binding have been planned
to ensure a sturdy, attractive publication which should
give years of enjoyment.
If your copy fails to meet our high standards,
please inform us and we will gladly replace it.

Music Sales' complete catalogue describes
thousands of titles and is available in full colour
sections by subject, direct from Music Sales Limited.
Please state your areas of interest and send
a cheque/postal order for £1.50 for postage to:
Music Sales Limited, Newmarket Road,
Bury St. Edmunds, Suffolk IP33 3YB.

www.musicsales.com

AWAY IN A MANGER

Words: Traditional
Music by William Kirkpatrick

Moderately

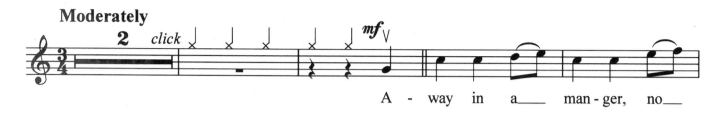

A - way in a__ man - ger, no__

crib for a bed, the__ lit - tle Lord Je - sus lay__

down his sweet head. The stars in the__ bright sky looked_

down where He lay, the__ lit - tle Lord Je - sus a -

sleep on the hay. The

cat - tle are__ low - ing, the__ ba - by a - wakes, but__

little Lord Jesus no___ cry-ing He makes. I

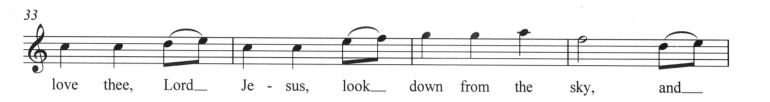

love thee, Lord__ Je-sus, look__ down from the sky, and__

stay by my side un-til__ morn-ing is nigh.

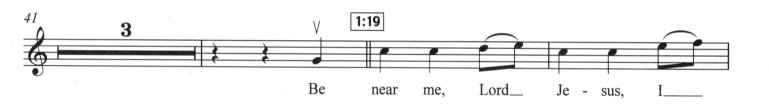

Be near me, Lord__ Je-sus, I___

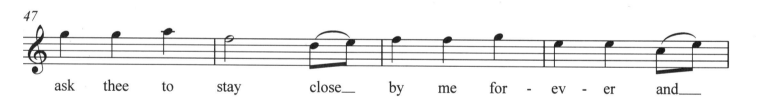

ask thee to stay close__ by me for-ev-er and__

love me, I pray. Bless all the dear__ chil-dren in__ Thy ten-der

care, and__ fit us for hea-ven to___ live with Thee there.

7

FROSTY THE SNOWMAN

Words & Music by Steve Nelson & Jack Rollins

Moderately

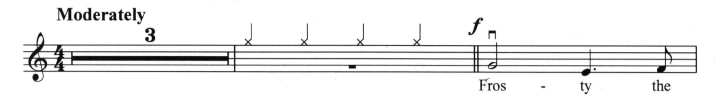

snow - man was a jol - ly hap - py soul. With a

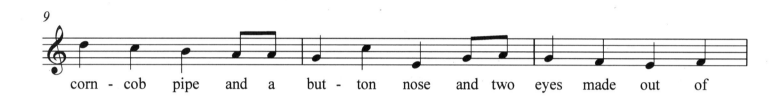

corn - cob pipe and a but - ton nose and two eyes made out of

coal. Fros - ty the snow - man is a

fai - ry tale they say. He was made of snow, but the

child - ren know how he came to life one day. There

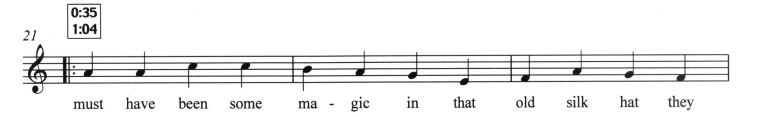

must have been some ma - gic in that old silk hat they

found, for when they placed it on his head, he be -

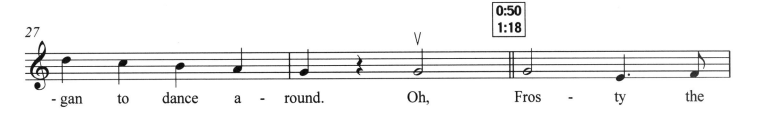

- gan to dance a - round. Oh, Fros - ty the

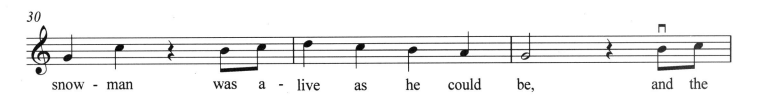

snow - man was a - live as he could be, and the

child - ren say he could laugh and play just the same as you and

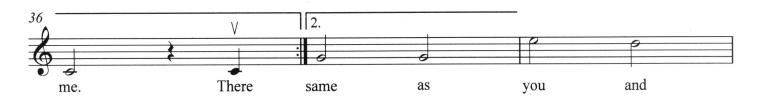

me. There same as you and

me.

GOOD KING WENCESLAS

Traditional

Moderately

Good King Wen - ces - las looked out

on the Feast of Ste - phen. When the snow lay round a - bout,

deep and crisp and e - ven. Bright - ly shone the moon that night,

though the wind was cru - el, when a poor man came in sight,

gath - 'ring win - ter fu - el. "Hi - ther, page and

stand by me if thou know'st it tell - ing. Yon - der pea - sant,

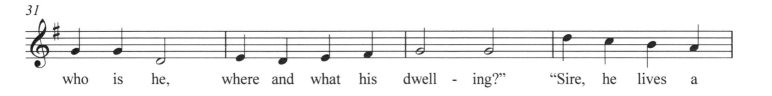

who is he, where and what his dwell - ing?" "Sire, he lives a

good league hence un - der - neath the moun - tain. Right a - gainst the

fo - rest fence by St. Ag - nes foun - - tain."

Page and mo - narch

forth they went, forth they went to - ge - ther. Through the rude wind's

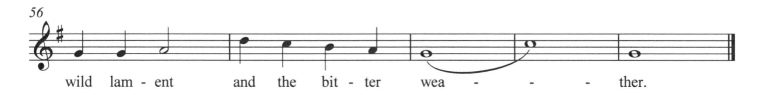

wild lam - ent and the bit - ter wea - - - ther.

HAPPY XMAS (WAR IS OVER)

Words & Music by John Lennon & Yoko Ono

I BELIEVE IN FATHER CHRISTMAS

Words & Music by Greg Lake & Peter Sinfield

I WISH IT COULD BE CHRISTMAS EVERY DAY

Words & Music by Roy Wood

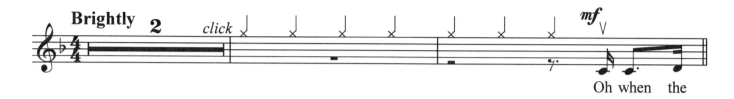

Oh when the

snow - man brings the snow, oh well he just might like to

know he's put a great big smile on some - bo - dy's

face.____ If you jump in - to your

bed, quick - ly cov - er up your head, don't you

lock the doors, you know that sweet San - ta Claus is on the way.____

Oh well I wish it could be Christ - mas ev - 'ry

day. When the kids start sing - ing and the

band be - gins to play. Oh I wish it could be

Christ - mas ev - 'ry day. So let the bells ring

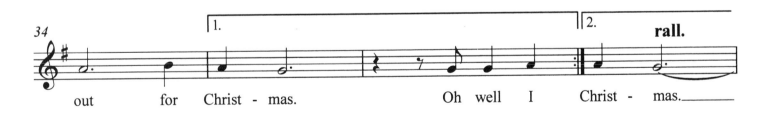

out for Christ - mas. Oh well I Christ - mas.

__ Why don't you give your love for Christ - mas?

JINGLE BELLS

Words & Music by J.S. Pierpont

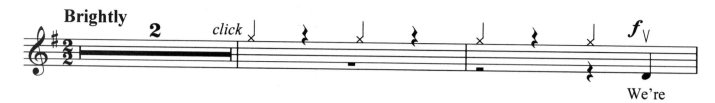

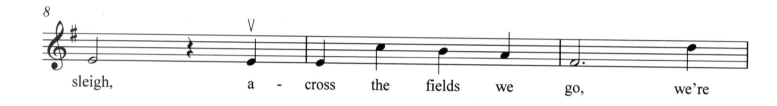

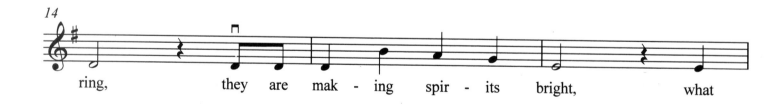

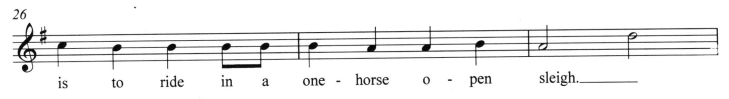

LAST CHRISTMAS

Words & Music by George Michael

ve - ry next day   you gave it a - way.___   This   year___   to

save me from tears   I'll give it to   some-one   spe - cial.

Last   Christ - mas   I gave you my heart, but the   ve - ry next day   you

gave it a - way.___   This   year___   to save me from tears   I'll

give it to   some-one   spe - cial.

MERRY XMAS EVERYBODY

Words & Music by Neville Holder & James Lea

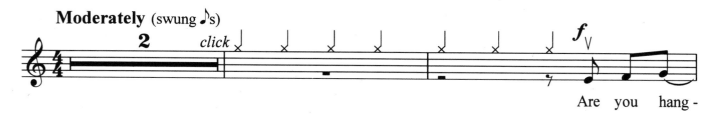

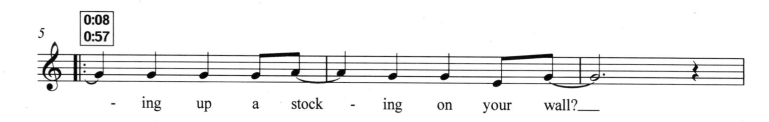

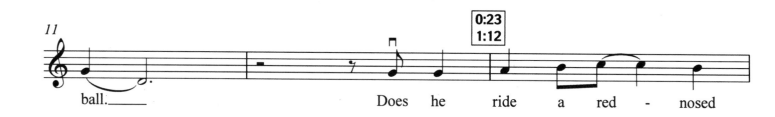

So here it is, Mer - ry Christ - mas, ev - 'ry -

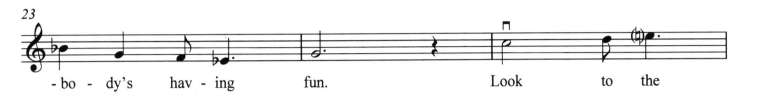

-bo - dy's hav - ing fun. Look to the

fu - ture now, it's on - ly just be - gun.

1.
Are you hang -
2.
So here it

is, Mer - ry Christ mas, ev - 'ry - bo - dy's hav - ing

fun. Look to the fu - ture now, it's

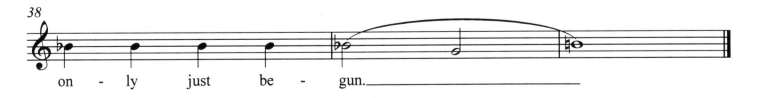

on - ly just be - gun.

MISTLETOE AND WINE

Words by Leslie Stewart & Jeremy Paul
Music by Keith Strachan

O LITTLE TOWN OF BETHLEHEM

Words by Phillips Brooks
Music by Lewis Redner

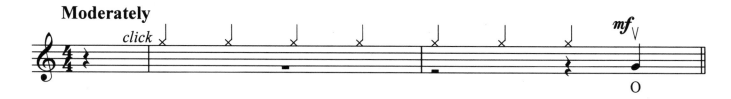

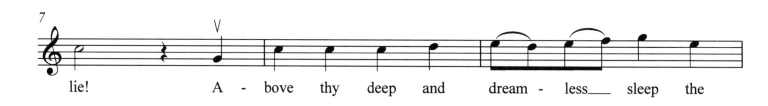

19

- night.   *mp* V

How

22 0:53

si - lent - ly, how si - lent - ly the wond - rous__ gift is

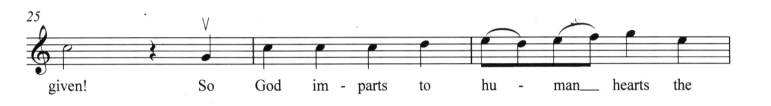

25

given! So God im - parts to hu - man__ hearts the

28   1:14

bless - ing__ of his heaven. No__ ear may hear__ His__

31

com - - ing, but in this world of sin where

34

meek souls will re - ceive__ Him__ still the dear Christ__ en - ters

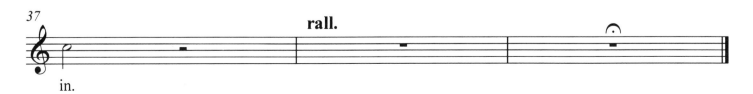

37   **rall.**

in.

SILENT NIGHT

Words by Joseph Mohr
Music by Franz Gruber

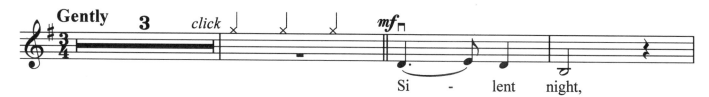

Si - lent night,

ho - ly night! All is calm,

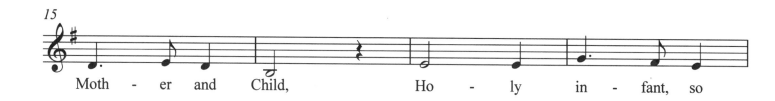

all is bright. Round yon Vir - gin

Moth - er and Child, Ho - ly in - fant, so

ten - der and mild. Sleep in heav - en - ly

peace.____ Sleep____ in heav - en - ly

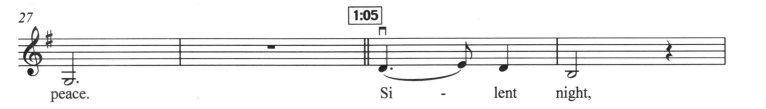

peace.   Si - lent night,

ho - ly night!   Shep - herds quake

at   the   sight.   Glo - ries stream____ from

Heav - en a - far,   Heav - n'ly hosts____ sing

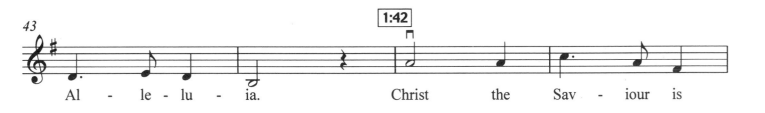

Al - le - lu - ia.   Christ   the   Sav - iour is

born!_____   Christ__ the   Sav - iour is born.

STOP THE CAVALRY

Words & Music by Jona Lewie

Hey, Mis - ter Chur - chill comes ov - er here

to say we're_ do - ing splen - did - ly. But it's ve - ry cold out here in the snow,

march - ing to and from the e - ne - my. Oh, I say it's tough, I have had e - nough,

can you stop the ca - val - ry? I have had to fight al - most ev - 'ry night

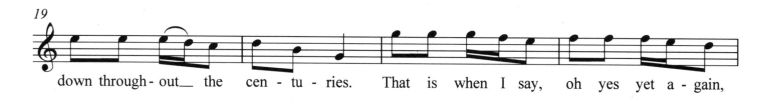

down through - out_ the cen - tu - ries. That is when I say, oh yes yet a - gain,

can you stop the ca - val - ry? Ma - ry proud - ly waits at home

in the nuc - le - ar fall - out zone. Wish I could_ be danc - ing now

in the arms_ of the girl I love._   Du bu du bu dum dum

du bu du bu dum, du bu dum dum du bu dum du bu du bu dum.

Du bu du bu dum dum   du bu du bu dum, du bu dum dum du bu dum

du bu du bu dum.   Wish I was at home___ for Christ - mas._____

Wish I could_ be danc - ing now in the arms_ of the girl I know.

Ma - ry proud - ly waits at home, she's been wait - ing two years long.___

Wish I was at home___ for Christ - mas._____

WINTER WONDERLAND

Words by Richard Smith
Music by Felix Bernard

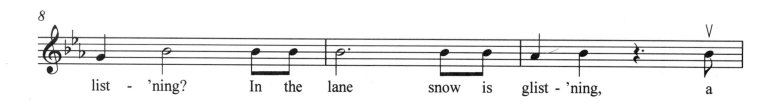

Sleigh bells ring, are you

list - 'ning? In the lane snow is glist - 'ning, a

beau - ti - ful sight,_ we're hap - py to - night,_ walk - in' in a win - ter won - der-

- land. Gone a - way is the blue - bird, here to stay is a

new bird, he sings a love song,_ as we go a - long,_

walk - in' in a win - ter won - der - land. In the mea - dow we can build a

snow - man, then pre - tend that he is Par - son Brown.

He'll say "Are you mar - ried?" We'll say "No, Man, but you can do the job when you're in

town." La - ter on we'll con - spire___ as we dream by the

fire___ to face un - a - fraid,_ the plans that we made,_

walk - in' in a win - ter won - der - land.

HARK! THE HERALD ANGELS SING

Music by Felix Mendelssohn
Words by Charles Wesley

Hark! The her - ald an - gels sing, "Glo ry to the

new born King! Peace on earth and mer - cy mild,__ God and sin - ners

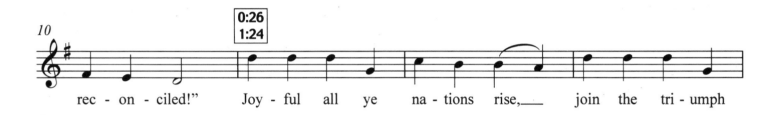

rec - on - ciled!" Joy - ful all ye na - tions rise,__ join the tri - umph

of the skies,__ with th'an - gel - ic host pro - claim, "Christ is__ born in

Beth - le - hem!" Hark! The her - ald an - gels sing, "Glo - ry__ to the

new born King!" "Glo - ry__ to the new born King!"

Printed by Printwise (Haverhill) Limited, Suffolk 7/05 (55655)

BEST OF
GUNS N' ROSES

Edited by Milton Okun

Management: Doug Goldstein/Big FD Entertainment, Inc.
Production: Daniel Rosenbaum/Rana Bernhardt
Art Direction: Rosemary Cappa-Jenkins/Jim Darling
Director of Music: Mark Phillips

Photography:
This page: Gene Kirkland
Facing page: Robert John

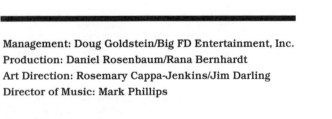

CONTENTS

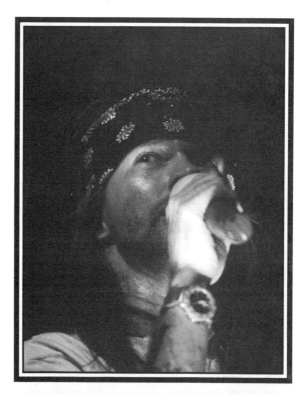

November Rain

Words and Music by
W. Axl Rose

* Recorded a half step lower

4

ken heart,— would-n't time— be out— to charm— you? Woh._____

And when your fears____ sub-side____ and shad-ows still____ re-main,

I know that you____ can love me when there's no one left to blame.

Sweet Child O' Mine

Words and Music by
W. Axl Rose, Slash, Izzy Stradlin',
Duff "Rose" McKagan and Steven Adler

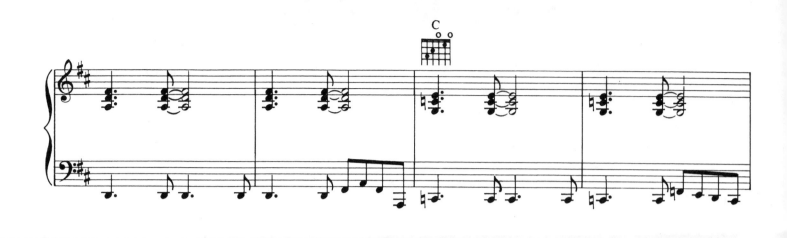

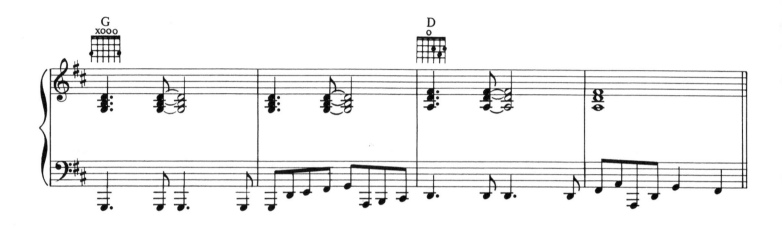

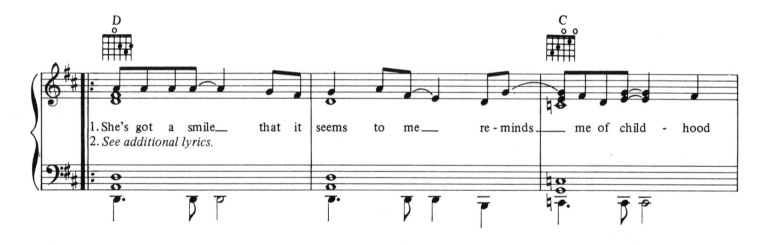

1.She's got a smile that it seems to me re-minds me of child - hood
2. *See additional lyrics.*

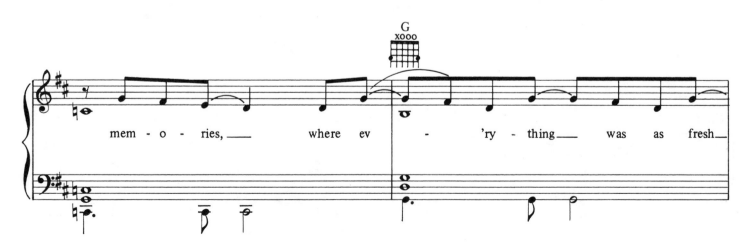

mem - o - ries, where ev - 'ry - thing was as fresh

as the bright blue sky.

Now and then when I see her face she takes me a - way to that

spe - cial place, and if I stared too long. I'll

prob - 'ly break down and cry.

Chorus

Whoa, whoa, whoa, sweet child o' mine.

Whoa, oh, oh, oh, sweet love o' mine.

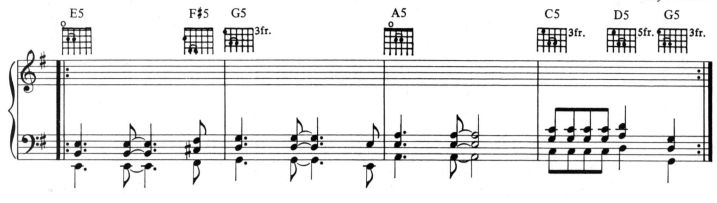

Where do we go?___ Where do we go___ now? Where do we go?___

p

Where do we go?___ Ah. _____

f

*Play 4 times
(w/vocal ad lib)*

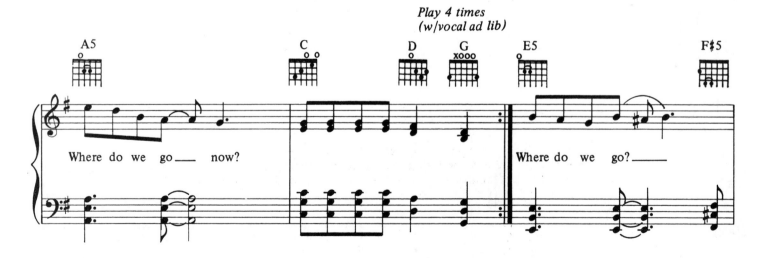

Where do we go___ now? Where do we go?___

Additional Lyrics

2. She's got eyes of the bluest skies, as if they thought of rain.
   I hate to look into those eyes and see an ounce of pain.
   Her hair reminds me of a warm safe place where as a child I'd hide,
   And pray for the thunder and the rain to quietly pass me by. *(To Chorus)*

Patience

Words and Music by
W. Axl Rose, Slash, Izzy Stradlin',
Duff "Rose" McKagan and Steven Adler

Said, sug-ar,___ make it slow___ and we come to-geth-er fine.___

All we need___ is just___ a lit-tle pa-

tience.

Moderately slow, in 4

D   D/F♯   G

Repeat and fade

* *Vocal ad lib (see additional lyrics)*

*Enter 3rd time

Additional Lyrics

2. I sit here on the stairs 'cause I'd rather be alone.
   If I can't have you right now I'll wait, dear.
   Sometimes I get so tense but I can't speed up the time.
   But you know, love, there's one more thing to consider.

   Said, woman, take it slow and things will be just fine.
   You and I'll just use a little patience.
   Said, sugar, take the time 'cause the lights are shining bright.
   You and I've got what it takes to make it.
   We won't fake it, ah, I'll never break it 'cause I can't take it.

   Vocal ad lib:

   Little patience, mm, yeah, mm, yeah.
   Need a little patience, yeah.
   Just a little patience, yeah.
   Some more patience.
   I been walkin' the streets at night
   Just tryin' to get it right.
   Hard to see with so many around.
   You know I don't like being stuck in the ground,
   And the streets don't change, but baby the name.
   I ain't got time for the game 'cause I need you.
   Yeah, yeah, but I need you, oo, I need you.
   Woh, I need you, oo, this time.

14 Years

Words and Music by
Izzy Stradlin' and W. Axl Rose

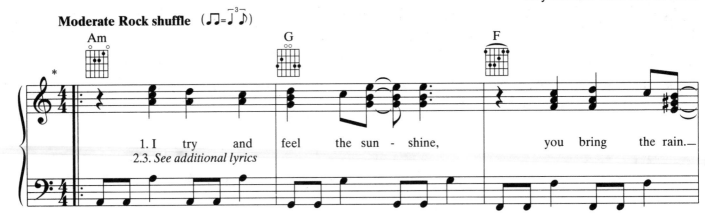

1. I try and feel the sun-shine, you bring the rain.—
2.3. *See additional lyrics*

— You try and hold me down—

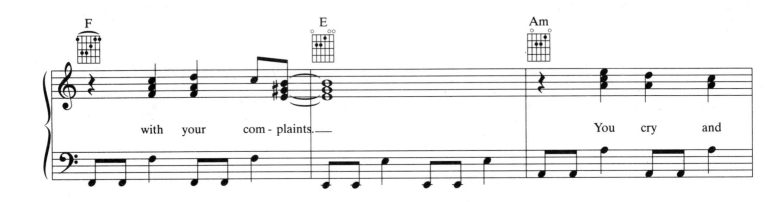

with your com-plaints.— You cry and

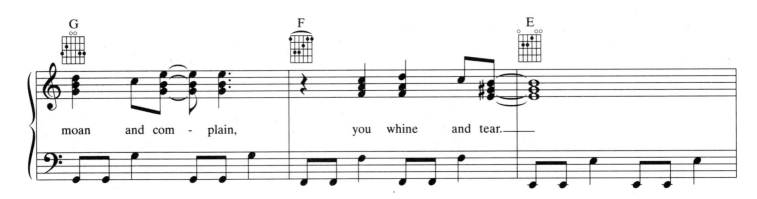

moan and com-plain, you whine and tear.—

* Recorded a half step lower.

26

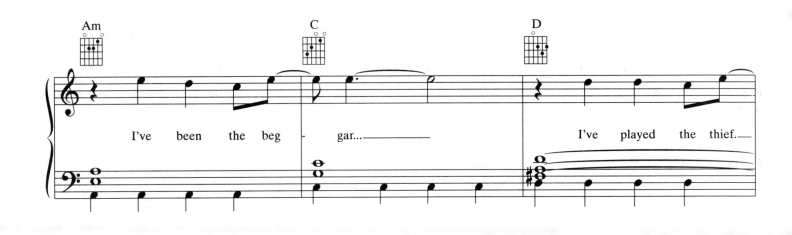

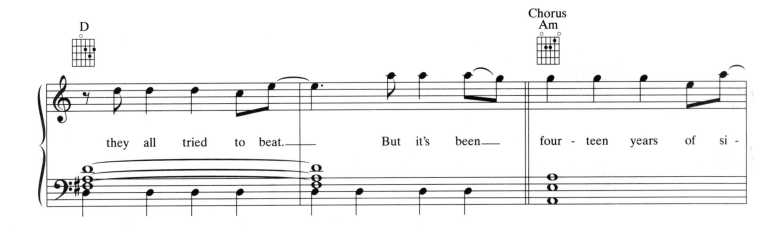

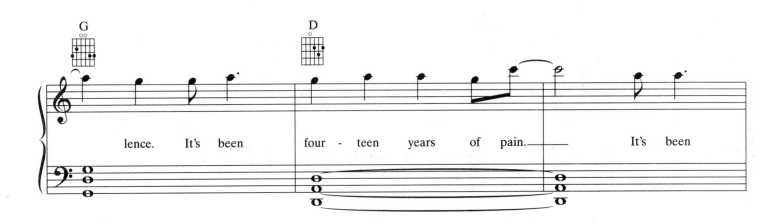

four - teen years that are gone for - ev - er and I'll never have a - gain,

well.

2nd time, D.C. al Coda

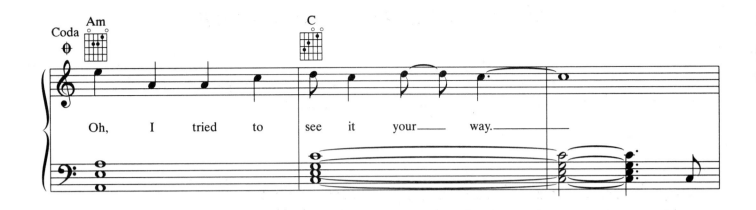

Oh, I tried to see it your____ way.____

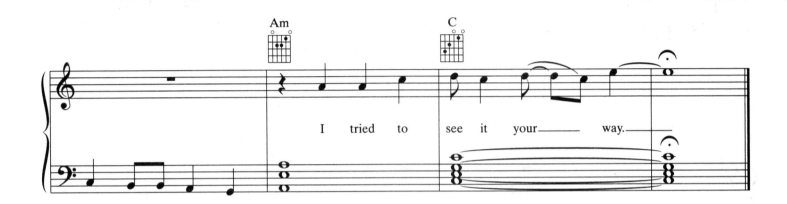

I tried to see it your____ way.____

Additional Lyrics

2. Your stupid girlfriends tell you that I'm to blame.
   Well, they're all used-up has-beens, out of the game.
   This time I'll have the last word, you hear what I say?
   I tried to see it your way, it won't work today.

   2nd Pre-chorus:
   You just don't step inside to 14 years.
   So hard to keep my own head... that's what I say.
   You know... I've been the dealer... hangin' on your street.
   I was the dog... they all tried to beat. *(To Chorus)*

3. Bullshit and contemplation, gossip's their trade.
   If they knew half the real truth, what would they say?
   Well, I'm past the point of concern, it's time to play.
   These last 4 years of madness sure put me straight.

   3rd Pre-chorus:
   Don't get back 14 years in just one day.
   So hard to keep my own head. Just go away.
   You know... just like a hooker, she said, "Nothin's for free."
   Oh, I tried to see it your way.
   I tried to see it your way.

Welcome To The Jungle

Words and Music by
W. Axl Rose, Slash, Izzy Stradlin',
Duff "Rose" McKagan and Steven Adler

Faster ♩ = 124

1. Wel-come to the jun-gle, we got fun 'n' games.
2.3. *See additional lyrics*

We got ev-'ry-thing you want,__ hon-ey, we know the names. We are the

sha na na na na na na na na na na na knees,   knees.___

Uh,   ah.   I wan-na watch you___ bleed.

I wan-na hear you___ scream!

I'm gon-na watch you bleed!

And when you're high____

____ you nev-er ev-er want to come down,____ so

down, — so down, — so down. _____

Yeah! _____

Now!

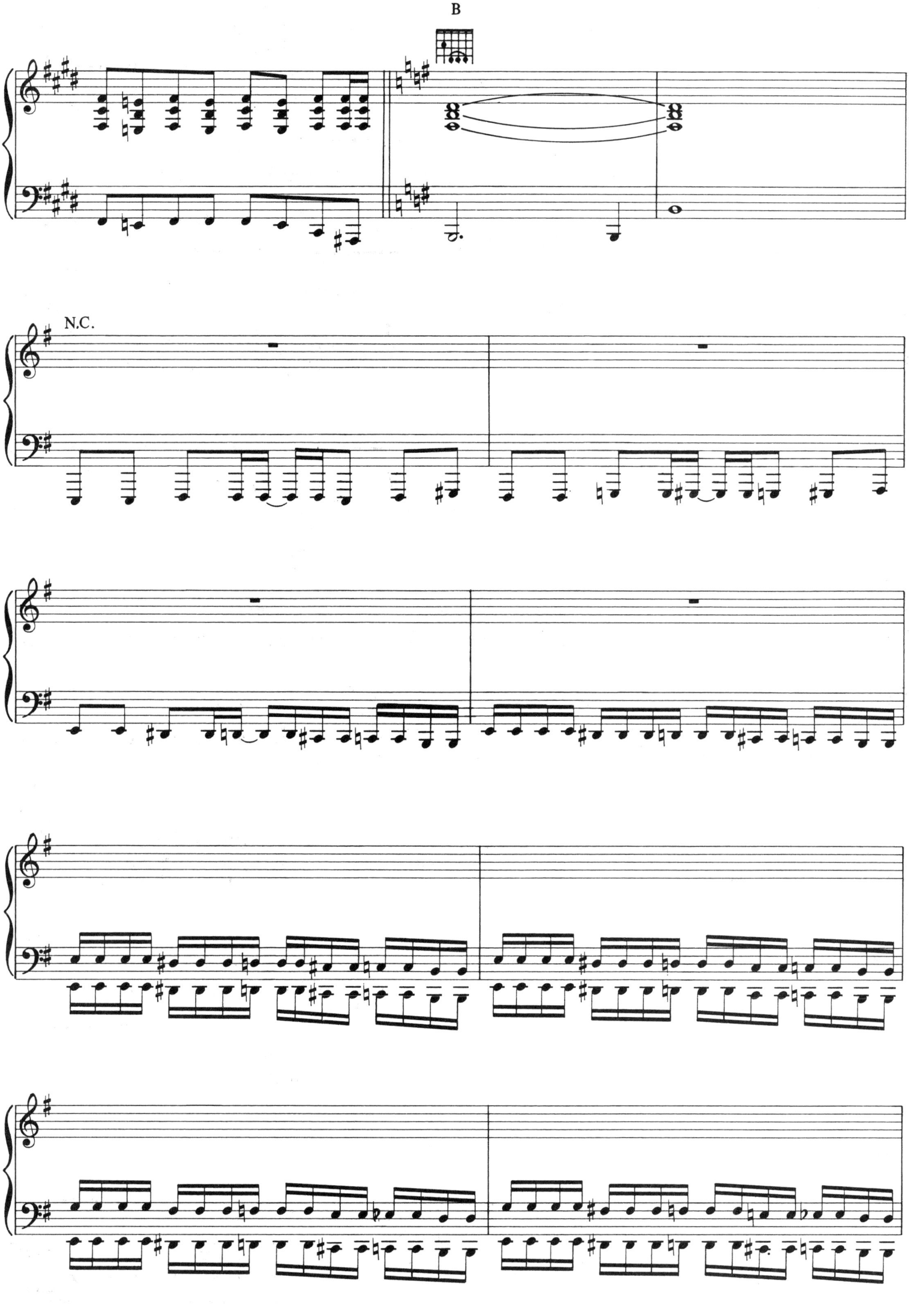
B
N.C.

You know where you are? You're in the jun - gle, ba - by!

F♯5 F5 F♯5 G5

You're gon - na die! _____

A5 G♯5 A5 B♭5 C5 D5

_____ In the jun - gle. Wel - come to the jun - gle. Watch it bring you to your

sha na na na na na na na na na na na knees, knees._ In the jun-

gle. Wel-come to the jun - gle. Feel_ my, oh, my, my,_

my ser-pen-tine._ Jun-gle. Wel-come to the jun - gle. Watch it bring you to your

Additional Lyrics

2. Welcome to the jungle, we take it day by day.
   If you want it, you're gonna bleed, but it's the price you pay.
   And you're a very sexy girl who's very hard to please.
   You can taste the bright lights, but you won't get them for free.
   In the jungle. Welcome to the jungle.
   Feel my, my, my serpentine.
   I wanna hear you scream!

3. Welcome to the jungle, it gets worse here every day.
   You learn to live like an animal in the jungle where we play.
   If you got a hunger for what you see, you'll take it eventually,
   You can have anything you want, but you better not take it from me.
   In the jungle. Welcome to the jungle.
   Watch it bring you to your sha na na na na na na na na na na na knees, knees.
   I'm gonna watch you bleed! *(To Bridge)*

Civil War

Words and Music by
Slash, Duff McKagan
and W. Axl Rose

Look at your young- men fight- ing. Look at your wom- en cry- ing.
Look at the hate— we're breed- ing. Look at the fear— we're feed- ing.

Look at your young- men dy- ing, the way they've al- ways done be- fore._
Look at the lives— we're lead- ing, the way we've al- ways done be- fore._

* Recorded a half step lower.

44

Estranged

Words and Music by
W. Axl Rose

Moderately slow

When you're talk - in' to your- self   and no - bod - y's

home,_____   you can   fool your - self.

You came in this world a-lone.

1.

mf

* Recorded a half step lower.

48

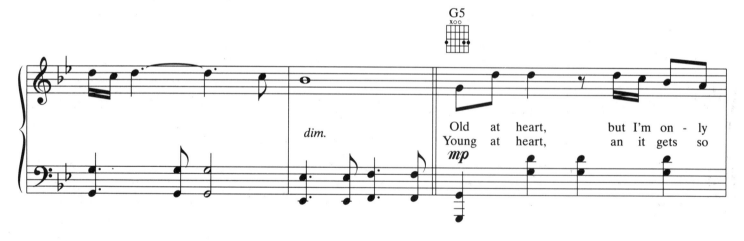

Old at heart, but I'm on - ly
Young at heart, an it gets so

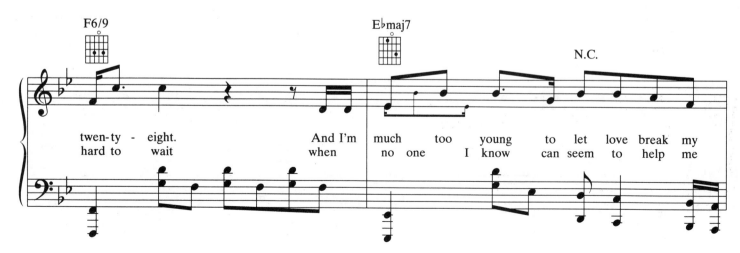

twen-ty - eight. And I'm much too young to let love break my
hard to wait when no one I know can seem to help me

How could you say that I nev - er need - ed you,

when you took ev - 'ry-thing,—

said, you took ev - 'ry-thing—— from me?——

out.—————— Still talk-in' to my-self

and no-bod-y's

home.————————

So no-bod-y ev-er told us, ba - by, how it was gon - na be.

So what-'ll hap-pen to— us, ba - by, guess we'll have to wait— and see.

1. When I find all of the rea-
2.3. *See additional lyrics*

sons, may-be I'll find— an-oth - er way,— find an-oth - er day.—

With all— the chang - ing sea - sons— of my life, may-be I'll get— it

1.
right next time.—

2.
for?

58

I'll nev-er find an-y-one to re- place you. Guess I'll have to make it thru this time, oh, this time

Additional Lyrics

2. An now that you've been broken down,
   Got your head out of the clouds,
   You're back down on the ground.
   And you don't talk so loud,
   An you don't walk so proud anymore,
   And what for?

3. Well, I jumped into the river
   Too many times to make it home.
   I'm out here on my own,
   An drifting all alone.
   If it doesn't show, give it time
   To read between the lines.

Paradise City

Words and Music by
W. Axl Rose, Slash, Izzy Stradlin',
Duff "Rose" McKagan and Steven Adler

Yeah. _

(Lead gtr. ad lib)

66

Double time ♩ = 208

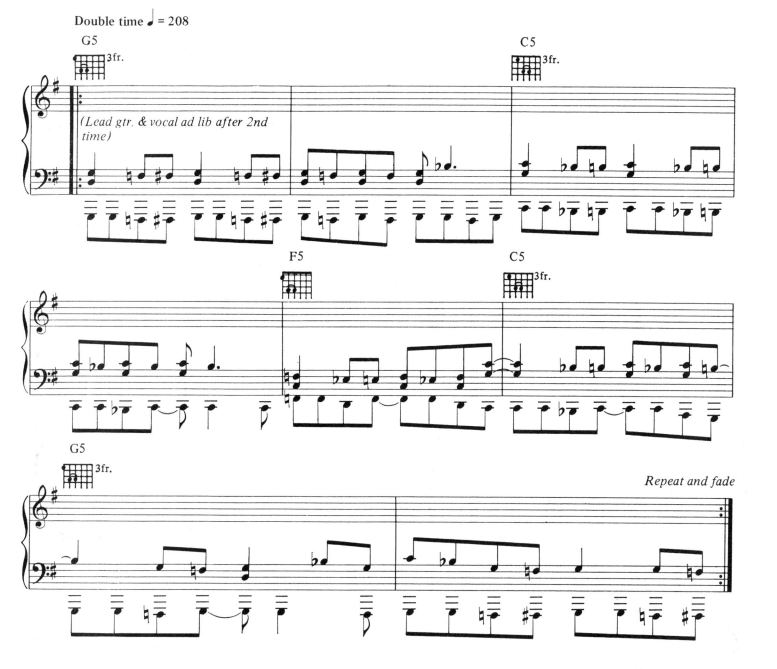

(Lead gtr. & vocal ad lib after 2nd time)

Repeat and fade

Additional Lyrics

2. Ragz to richez, or so they say.
   Ya gotta keep pushin' for the fortune and fame.
   It's all a gamble when it's just a game.
   Ya treat it like a capital crime.
   Everybody's doin' their time. *(To Chorus)*

3. Strapped in the chair of the city's gas chamber,
   Why I'm here I can't quite remember.
   The surgeon general says it's hazarous to breathe.
   I'd have anothe cigarette but I can't see.
   Tell me who ya gonna believe? *(To Chorus)*

4. Captain America's been torn a part.
   Now he's a court jester with a broken heart.
   He said, "Turn me around and take me back to the start."
   I must be losin' my mind. "Are you blind?"
   I've seen it all a million times. *(To Chorus)*

Yesterdays

Words and Music by
West Arkeen, Del James,
Billy McCloud and W. Axl Rose

Moderately slow Rock

* Recorded a half step lower.

got noth-in' for me. ____ Yes-ter- day,–

_____ yeah. _____

Repeat and fade

Additional Lyrics

2. Prayers in my pocket
   And no hand in destiny.
   I'll keep on movin' along
   With no time to plant my feet.
   'Cause yesterday's got nothin' for me.
   Old pictures that I'll always see.
   Some things could be better
   If we'd all just let them be. *(To Chorus)*

3. Yesterday there were so many things
   I was never shown.
   Suddenly this time I found
   I'm on the streets and I'm all alone.
   Yesterday's got nothin' for me.
   Old pictures that I'll always see.
   I ain't got time to reminisce
   Old novelties. *(To Chorus)*

Don't Cry (Original)

Words and Music by
Izzy Stradlin' and W. Axl Rose

Cherry Lane Music

• Quality In Printed Music •